Mighty Mighty MONSTERS

THE TOY SNATCHER

Raintree

www.raintreepublishers.co.uk
Visit our website to find out
more information about
Raintree books.

To order:
☎ Phone 0845 6044371
🖹 Fax +44 (0) 1865 312263
✉ Email myorders@raintreepublishers.co.uk

Customers from outside the UK please telephone +44 1865 312262

Raintree is an imprint of Capstone Global Library Limited,
a company incorporated in England and Wales having its registered
office at 7 Pilgrim Street, London, EC4V 6LB
– Registered company number: 6695582

First published by Stone Arch Books in 2010
First published in the United Kingdom in paperback in 2012
The moral rights of the proprietor have been asserted.

Edited by Siân Smith
Originated by Capstone Global Library Ltd
Printed and bound in China by South China Printing Company

ISBN 978 1 406 24230 0 (paperback)
16 15 14 13 12
10 9 8 7 6 5 4 3 2 1

British Library Cataloguing in Publication Data
O'Reilly, Sean, 1974
741.5-dc23
A full catalogue record for this book is available
from the British Library

THE TOY SNATCHER

created by
Sean O'Reilly

illustrated by
Arcana Studio

In a strange corner of the world known as Transylmania . . .

Legendary monsters were born.

WELCOME TO TRANSYLMANIA

But long before their frightful fame, these classic creatures faced fears of their own.

To take on terrifying teachers and homework horrors,
they formed the most fearsome friendship on Earth . . .

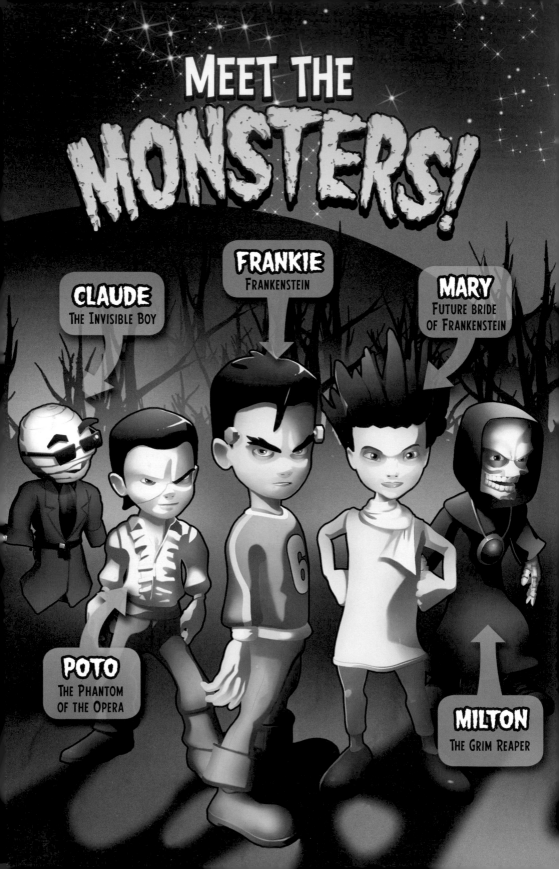

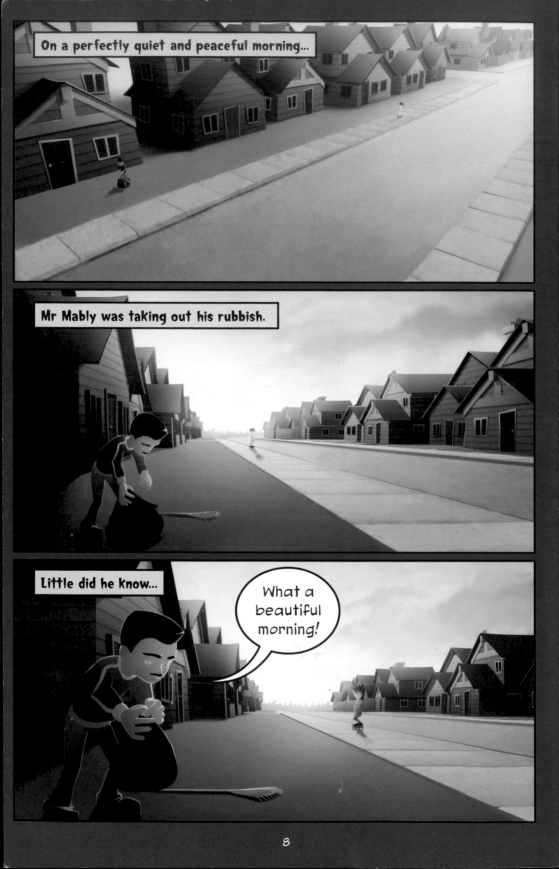

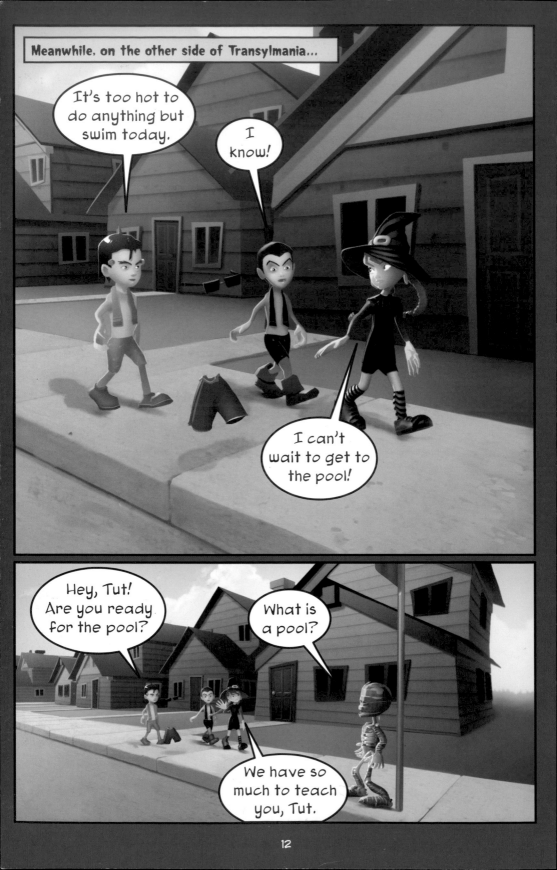

13

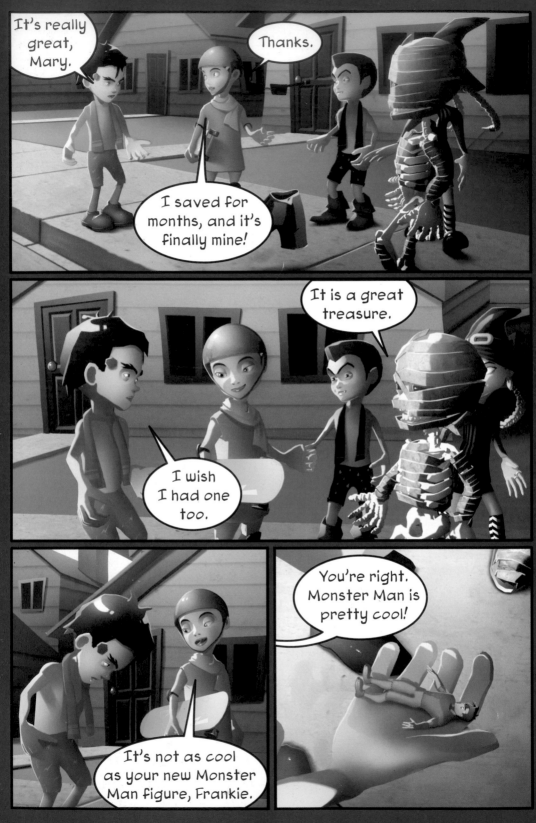

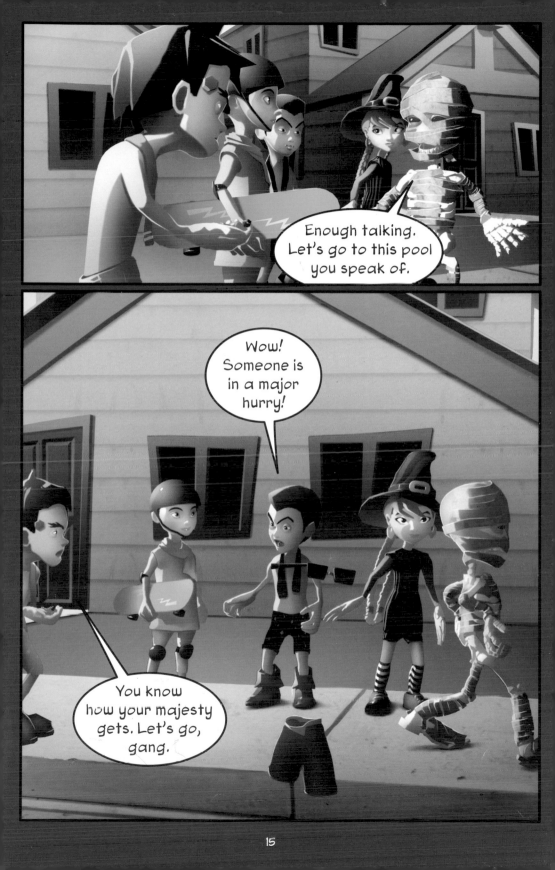

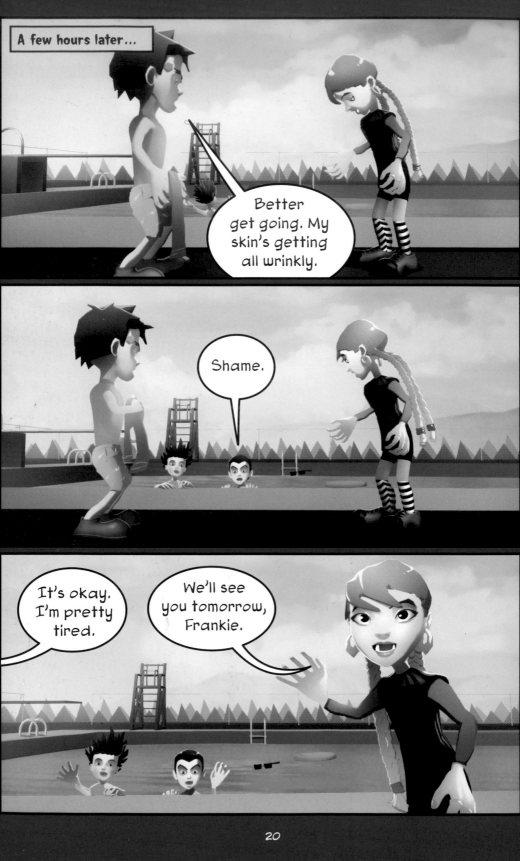

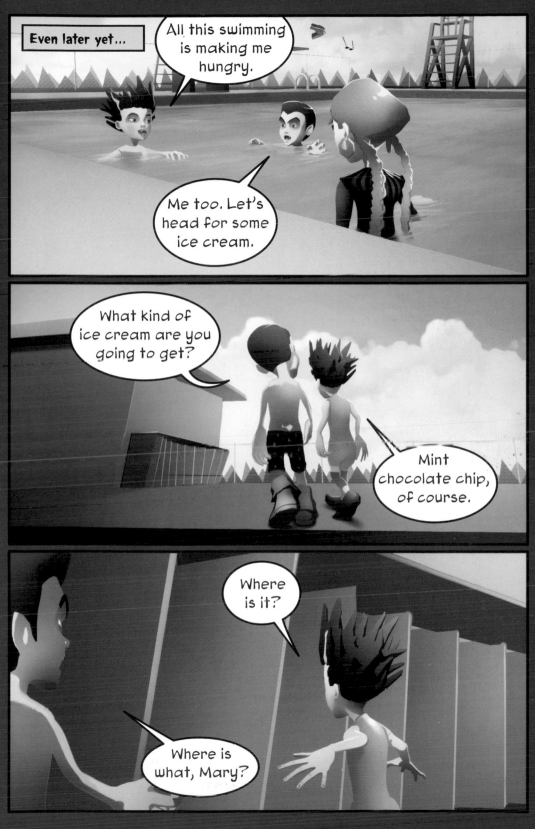

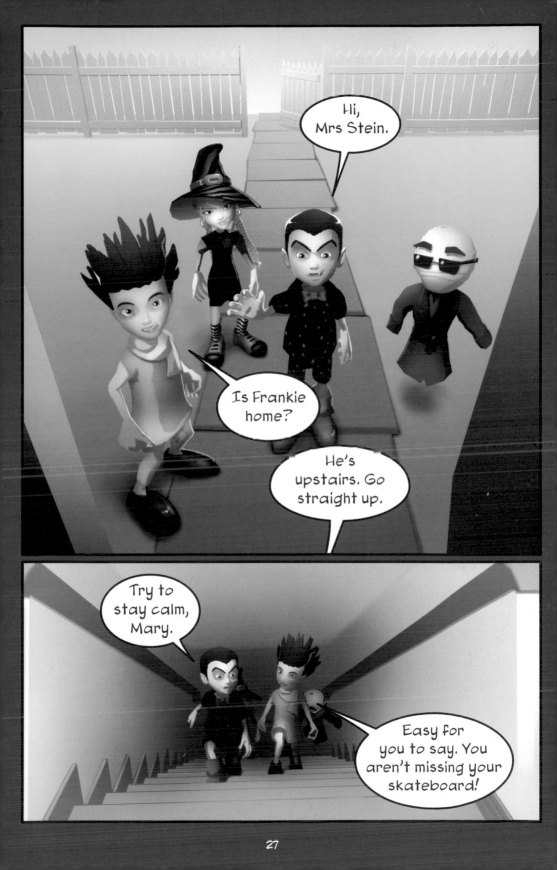

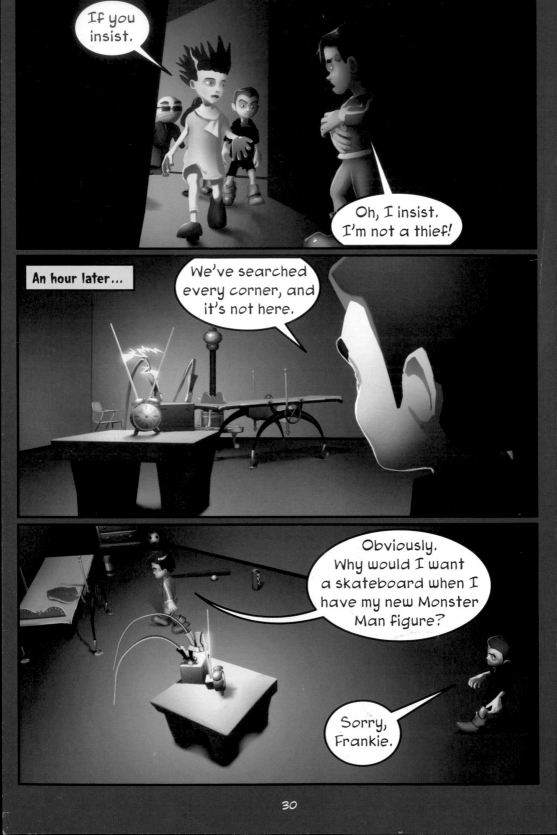

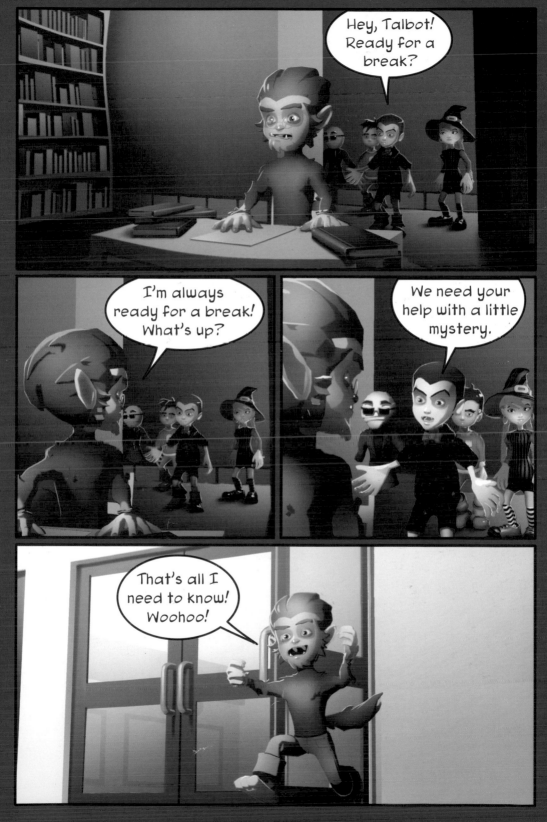

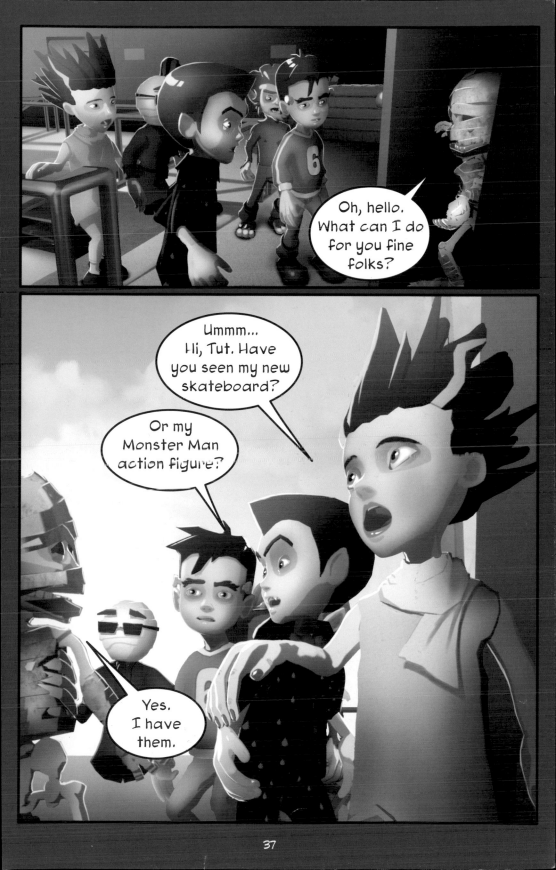

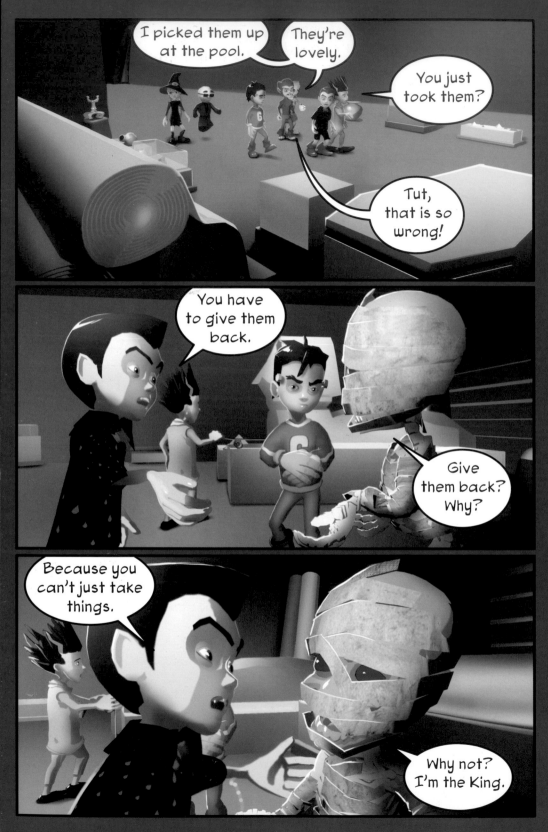

Even if you are a king, that's called stealing.
I'm so sorry! I had no idea.
Everyone just really liked the new treasures, so I wanted them for my collection.
Oh, Tut. You have so much to learn.
I'm so sorry, Frankie. Can you forgive me?
I just got all crazy about my skateboard.
It's okay, Mary. Friends forgive.

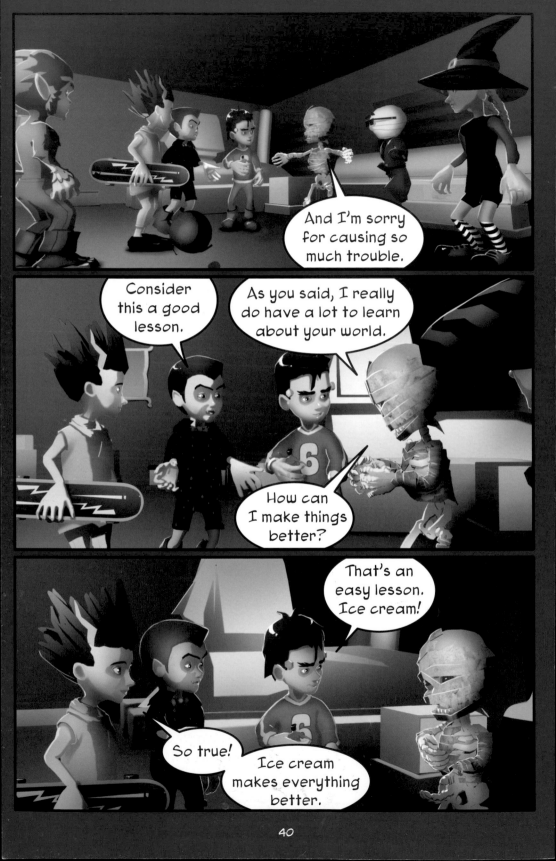

SKATEBOARD
EQUIPMENT

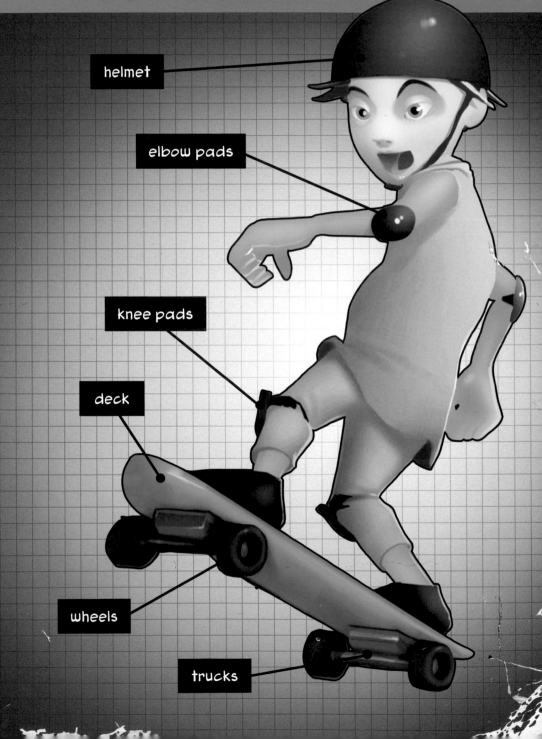

helmet

elbow pads

knee pads

deck

wheels

trucks

GLOSSARY

accusation a charge of wrongdoing

adventure an exciting experience

brittle easily snapped or broken

disappear to go out of sight

explanation a statement that makes something clear

insist to demand something firmly

majesty the formal title for a king or a queen

stealing taking something that isn't yours

treasure valuable things that have been collected or hidden

DISCUSSION QUESTIONS

1. When Mary couldn't find her skateboard, she blamed
   Frankie. Why did Mary blame her friend? How do you
   think that made Frankie feel?

2. Have you ever accused someone of doing something
   they didn't do? Explain what happened.

3. Were you surprised when you found out what happened
   to the missing items? Why or why not?

WRITING PROMPTS

1. Mary loves her new skateboard, and Frankie loves his
   new Monster Man action figure. Write a paragraph
   about your favourite toy.

2. Mary bought the skateboard with money that she had
   saved, which made the skateboard even more special.
   Make a list of five jobs you could do to earn money.

3. Pretend you are Mary, and write an apology letter
   to Frankie.

FIND OUT MORE

INFORMATION BOOKS

The Mystery of Vampires and Werewolves
(Can Science Solve?), Chris Oxlade (Heinemann
Library, 2008)

Vampires and the Undead (Dark Side), Anita Ganeri
(Wayland, 2010)

GRAPHIC NOVELS

Dracula (Graphic Revolve), Bram Stoker, retold by
Michael Burgan (Raintree, 2009)

Frankenstein (Graphic Revolve), Mary Shelley, retold
by Michael Burgan (Raintree, 2009)

The Invisible Man, (Graphic Chillers), H. G. Wells,
retold by Joeming Dunn (Franklin Watts, 2010)

WEBSITE

learnenglishkids.britishcouncil.org/en/make-
your-own/make-your-monster
Visit this website to create your own monster. You
can also invent your own scary story, dangerous
animal, or superhero.

Mighty Mighty MONSTERS ADVENTURES

Hide and Shriek!
ISBN: 978 1 406 23718 4

Lost in Spooky Forest
ISBN: 978 1 406 23720 7

The King of Halloween Castle
ISBN: 978 1 406 23719 1

New Monster in School
ISBN: 978 1 406 23723 8

Monster Mansion
ISBN: 978 1 406 23721 4

My Missing Monster
ISBN: 978 1 406 23722 1

The Missing Mummy
ISBN: 978 1 406 24227 0

Monster Beach
ISBN: 978 1 406 24226 3

The Monster Crooks
ISBN: 978 1 406 24228 7

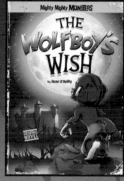

The Wolfboy's Wish
ISBN: 978 1 406 24231 7

The Toy Snatcher
ISBN: 978 1 406 24230 0

The Scare Fair
ISBN: 978 1 406 24229 4

They're Fang-tastic!

ABOUT
SEAN O'REILLY
AND ARCANA STUDIO

As a lifelong comics fan, Sean O'Reilly dreamed of becoming a comic book creator. In 2004, he realized that dream by creating Arcana Studio. In one short year, O'Reilly took his studio from a one-person operation in his house to an award-winning comic book publisher with more than 150 graphic novels produced for Harper Collins, Simon & Schuster, Random House, Scholastic, and others.

Within a year, the company won many awards including the Shuster Award for Outstanding Publisher and the Moonbeam Award for top children's graphic novel. O'Reilly also won the Top 40 Under 40 award from the city of Vancouver and authored *The Clockwork Girl* for Top Graphic Novel at Book Expo America in 2009.

Currently, O'Reilly is one of the most prolific independent comic book writers in Canada. While showing no signs of slowing down in comics, he now also writes screenplays and adapts his creations for the big screen.